Andrew Brodie Basics

LET'S DO MULTIPLICATION AND DIVISION

FOR AGES 9–10

with over **100** reward stickers

- Over 400 practice questions
- Regular progress tests
- Matched to the National Curriculum

Published 2016 by Bloomsbury Publishing Plc
50 Bedford Square, London, WC1B 3DP

www.bloomsbury.com

Bloomsbury is a registered trademark of Bloomsbury Publishing Plc

ISBN 978-1-4729-2636-4

Copyright © 2016 Bloomsbury Publishing
Text copyright © 2016 Andrew Brodie
Cover and inside illustrations of Maurice the Mouse and Andrew Brodie
© 2016 Nikalas Catlow. Other inside illustrations © 2016 Cathy Hughes

A CIP catalogue for this book is available from the British Library.

10 9 8 7 6 5 4 3 2 1

Printed in China by Leo Paper Products

This book is produced using paper that is made from wood grown in managed, sustainable forests. It is natural, renewable and recyclable. The logging and manufacturing processes conform to the environmental regulations of the country of origin.

To see our full range of titles visit **www.bloomsbury.com**

BLOOMSBURY

Introduction

This is the fifth in the series of *Andrew Brodie Basics: Let's Do Multiplication and Division* books. Each book contains more than 400 maths questions, deliberately designed to cover the following key aspects of the 'Number' section of the National Curriculum:

- Number and place value
- Multiplication and division.

Your child will get the most out of this series if you make time to discuss number knowledge as well as basic multiplication and division questions with them. Talk about real life situations, such as how many eggs there would be in sixteen boxes of six. Does your child recognise that the question can be split into a) finding the number of eggs in ten boxes and b) finding the number in six boxes, then adding together the two answers? Mathematically, this can be shown as $16 \times 6 = 10 \times 6 + 6 \times 6$. This is known as the Distributive Law.

In Year 5 it is important that the children continue to practise the times tables, together with the related division facts: they should now know all of the times tables, two to twelve, up to twelve times twelve. They will use their tables knowledge to identify multiples, factors and prime numbers as well as square numbers and cube numbers.

The level of difficulty is increased gradually throughout the book but note that some questions are repeated. For example, the multiplication tables, together with the related division facts, will appear lots of times. This is to ensure that children have the opportunity to learn vital new facts: they may not know the answer to a particular question the first time they encounter it but this provides the opportunity for you to help them to learn it for the next time that they come across it. Don't be surprised if they need to practise certain questions many times.

You may find that your child is challenged by some questions. Make sure that they don't feel unhappy about this. Instead, encourage them not to worry about making mistakes but to learn from them.

In Year 5, children extend their skills by using the facts they know to solve related questions. They solve problems involving multiplication and division and they learn to multiply numbers up to four digits by a one-digit or two-digit number, using the processes of short multiplication and long multiplication. They also practise short division, dividing numbers up to four digits by a one-digit number and finding remainders where appropriate.

Children gain confidence by learning facts that they can use in their work. With lots of practice they will see their score improve and will learn to find maths both satisfying and enjoyable.

Look out for....

Maurice the Mouse, who provides useful tips and helpful advice throughout.

Brodie's Fast Five, quick-fire questions designed to test your child's mental arithmetic.

Practising the two times table

1 Write out the two times table as fast as you can. Time yourself.

1 × 2 =		
2 × 2 =		

Time taken ◯ Seconds

All the answers above are called multiples of two.

2 Write out the answers to the two times table division facts as fast as you can. Time yourself.

2 ÷ 2 =	10 ÷ 2 =	18 ÷ 2 =
4 ÷ 2 =	12 ÷ 2 =	20 ÷ 2 =
6 ÷ 2 =	14 ÷ 2 =	22 ÷ 2 =
8 ÷ 2 =	16 ÷ 2 =	24 ÷ 2 =

Time taken ◯ Seconds

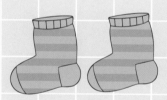

3 How many socks are needed to make eight pairs?

4 How many pairs can be made if there are twenty-four matching socks?

5 How many socks are needed to make eleven pairs?

6 How many pairs can be made if there are eighteen matching socks?

7 How many socks are needed to make fifteen pairs?

8 How many pairs can be made if there are forty matching socks?

Do you know the three times table?

1 Write out the three times table as fast as you can. Time yourself.

$1 \times 3 =$

$2 \times 3 =$

Time taken Seconds

All the answers above are called **multiples** of three.

2 Write out the answers to the three times table division facts as fast as you can. Time yourself.

$3 \div 3 \ =$ $6 \div 3 \ =$ $18 \div 3 =$

$36 \div 3 =$ $33 \div 3 =$ $30 \div 3 =$

$12 \div 3 =$ $21 \div 3 =$ $15 \div 3 =$

$27 \div 3 =$ $9 \div 3 \ =$ $24 \div 3 =$

Time taken Seconds

A tricycle has three wheels.

3 How many wheels are needed to make seven tricycles?

4 How many tricycles can be made if there are twenty-four wheels?

5 How many wheels are needed to make twelve tricycles?

6 How many tricycles can be made if there are eighteen wheels?

7 How many wheels are needed to make nine tricycles?

8 How many tricycles can be made if there are thirty-six wheels?

9 How many wheels are needed to make thirty tricycles?

10 How many tricycles can be made if there are sixty wheels?

Practising the four times table

1 **Write out the four times table as fast as you can. Time yourself.**

1 x 4 =

2 x 4 =

Time taken
Seconds

All the answers above are called multiples of four.

2 **Write out the answers to the four times table division facts as fast as you can. Time yourself.**

48 ÷ 4 =   24 ÷ 4 =   44 ÷ 4 =

36 ÷ 4 =   40 ÷ 4 =   32 ÷ 4 =

16 ÷ 4 =   12 ÷ 4 =   20 ÷ 4 =

4 ÷ 4 =   8 ÷ 4 =   28 ÷ 4 =

Time taken
Seconds

A car has four wheels.

3 **How many wheels are needed to make eight cars?**

7 **How many wheels are needed to make nine cars?**

4 **How many cars can be made if there are twenty-four wheels?**

8 **How many cars can be made if there are 36 wheels?**

5 **How many wheels are needed to make twelve cars?**

9 **How many wheels are needed to make twenty cars?**

6 **How many cars can be made if there are sixteen wheels?**

10 **How many cars can be made if there are sixty wheels?**

Do you know the five times table?

1 Write out the five times table as fast as you can. Time yourself.

$1 \times 5 =$

$2 \times 5 =$

Time taken — Seconds

All the answers above are called **multiples** of five.

2 Write out the answers to the five times table division facts as fast as you can. Time yourself.

$50 \div 5 =$ $5 \div 5 =$ $35 \div 5 =$

$60 \div 5 =$ $30 \div 5 =$ $20 \div 5 =$

$15 \div 5 =$ $55 \div 5 =$ $45 \div 5 =$

$25 \div 5 =$ $40 \div 5 =$ $10 \div 5 =$

Time taken — Seconds

There are five pears in a bag.

3 How many pears are needed to fill nine bags?

4 How many bags can be filled if there are twenty-five pears?

5 How many pears are needed to fill six bags?

6 How many bags can be filled if there are fifty-five pears?

7 How many pears are needed to fill twelve bags?

8 How many bags can be filled if there are sixty-five pears?

9 How many pears are needed to fill fifteen bags?

10 How many bags can be filled if there are a hundred pears?

Do you know the six times table?

1 Write out the six times table as fast as you can. Time yourself.

1 x 6 =		
2 x 6 =		

Time taken Seconds

All the answers above are called multiples of six.

2 Write out the answers to the six times table division facts as fast as you can. Time yourself.

36 ÷ 6 =   42 ÷ 6 =   12 ÷ 6 =

66 ÷ 6 =   54 ÷ 6 =   30 ÷ 6 =

18 ÷ 6 =   72 ÷ 6 =   6 ÷ 6 =

24 ÷ 6 =   60 ÷ 6 =   48 ÷ 6 =

Time taken Seconds

There are six eggs in a box.

3 How many eggs are needed to fill nine boxes?

4 How many boxes can be filled if there are twenty-four eggs?

5 How many eggs are needed to fill six boxes?

6 How many boxes can be filled if there are sixty-six eggs?

7 How many eggs are needed to fill twelve boxes?

8 How many boxes can be filled if there are forty-two eggs?

9 How many eggs are needed to fill fifteen boxes?

10 How many boxes can be filled if there are eighty-four eggs?

Complete each set of questions as quickly as you can.

Set A

1. 6 x 2 =
2. 24 ÷ 2 =
3. 12 x 2 =
4. 18 ÷ 2 =
5. 12 x 3 =
6. 33 ÷ 3 =
7. 8 x 3 =
8. 6 ÷ 3 =
9. 6 x 3 =
10. 27 ÷ 3 =
11. 5 x 3 =
12. 21 ÷ 3 =

Set B

1. 4 x 4 =
2. 40 ÷ 4 =
3. 9 x 4 =
4. 48 ÷ 4 =
5. 7 x 4 =
6. 4 x 4 =
7. 12 ÷ 4 =
8. 11 x 5 =
9. 45 ÷ 5 =
10. 5 x 5 =
11. 60 ÷ 5 =
12. 9 x 5 =

Set C

1. 6 x 6 =
2. 60 ÷ 6 =
3. 12 x 6 =
4. 42 ÷ 6 =
5. 30 x 2 =
6. 23 x 3 =
7. 18 x 2 =
8. 80 x 4 =
9. 30 x 5 =
10. 90 x 2 =
11. 70 x 6 =
12. 40 x 4 =

Time taken — Seconds

Time taken — Seconds

Time taken — Seconds

13. In a class of thirty children, how many groups of three children can be made?

14. In a class of thirty children, how many groups of six children can be made?

15. In a class of thirty children, how many groups of five children can be made?

16. In a class of thirty children, how many groups of two children can be made?

Practising the seven times table

Do you know the seven times table?

1 Write out the seven times table as fast as you can. Time yourself.

$1 \times 7 =$

$2 \times 7 =$

Time taken **Seconds**

All the answers above are called **multiples** of seven.

2 Write out the answers to the seven times table division facts as fast as you can. Time yourself.

$49 \div 7 =$ $56 \div 7 =$ $35 \div 7 =$

$70 \div 7 =$ $63 \div 7 =$ $84 \div 7 =$

$14 \div 7 =$ $21 \div 7 =$ $77 \div 7 =$

$7 \div 7 \ =$ $42 \div 7 =$ $28 \div 7 =$

Time taken **Seconds**

There are seven days in a week.

3 How many days are there altogether in four weeks?

4 How many weeks are made up of a total of fifty-six days?

5 How many days are there altogether in nine weeks?

6 How many weeks are made up of a total of seventy days?

7 How many days are there altogether in six weeks?

8 How many weeks are made up of a total of thirty-five days?

9 How many days are there altogether in twenty weeks?

10 How many weeks are made up of a total of one hundred and forty days?

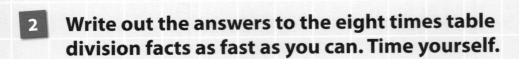

All of the answers to question one are called 'multiples' of eight.

1 Write out the eight times table as fast as you can. Time yourself.

1 x 8 =

2 x 8 =

Time taken — Seconds

2 Write out the answers to the eight times table division facts as fast as you can. Time yourself.

64 ÷ 8 =   40 ÷ 8 =   96 ÷ 8 =

88 ÷ 8 =   16 ÷ 8 =   48 ÷ 8 =

24 ÷ 8 =   8 ÷ 8 =   80 ÷ 8 =

72 ÷ 8 =   56 ÷ 8 =   32 ÷ 8 =

Time taken — Seconds

There are eight iced buns in a pack.

3 How many iced buns are there altogether in four packs?

4 How many packs can be filled from a total of fifty-six iced buns?

5 How many iced buns are there altogether in nine packs?

6 How many packs can be filled from a total of ninety-six iced buns?

7 How many iced buns are there altogether in eight packs?

8 How many packs can be filled from a total of one hundred and sixty iced buns?

9 How many iced buns are there altogether in fourteen packs?

10 How many packs can be filled from a total of two hundred iced buns?

All of the answers to question one are called 'multiples' of nine.

1 Write out the nine times table as fast as you can. Time yourself.

$1 \times 9 =$

$2 \times 9 =$

Time taken — Seconds

2 Write out the answers to the nine times table division facts as fast as you can. Time yourself.

$54 \div 9 =$ $63 \div 9 =$ $18 \div 9 =$

$45 \div 9 =$ $108 \div 9 =$ $90 \div 9 =$

$99 \div 9 =$ $9 \div 9 =$ $36 \div 9 =$

$27 \div 9 =$ $72 \div 9 =$ $81 \div 9 =$

Time taken — Seconds

There are nine cupcakes in a pack.

3 How many cupcakes are there altogether in three packs?

4 How many packs can be filled from a total of fifty-four cupcakes?

5 How many cupcakes are there altogether in eleven packs?

6 How many packs can be filled from a total of eighty-one cupcakes?

7 How many cupcakes are there altogether in eight packs?

8 How many packs can be filled from a total of one hundred and seventeen cupcakes?

9 How many cupcakes are there altogether in fourteen packs?

10 How many packs can be filled from a total of one hundred and eighty cupcakes?

Do you know the eleven times table?

1 Write out the eleven times table as fast as you can.
Time yourself.

1 x 11 =		
2 x 11 =		

Time taken — Seconds

All the answers above are called multiples of eleven.

2 Write out the answers to the eleven times table division facts as fast as you can. Time yourself.

121 ÷ 11 =	11 ÷ 11 =	77 ÷ 11 =
22 ÷ 11 =	55 ÷ 11 =	44 ÷ 11 =
66 ÷ 11 =	110 ÷ 11 =	99 ÷ 11 =
33 ÷ 11 =	88 ÷ 11 =	132 ÷ 11 =

Time taken — Seconds

Each football team has eleven players.

3 How many players are needed for eight teams?

7 How many players are needed for eleven teams?

4 How many teams can be made if there are twenty-two players?

8 How many teams can be made if there are one hundred and ten players?

5 How many players are needed for three teams?

9 How many players are needed for twelve teams?

6 How many teams can be made if there are ninety-nine players?

10 How many teams can be made if there are seventy-seven players?

12

Practising the twelve times table

Do you know the twelve times table?

1 Write out the twelve times table as fast as you can. Time yourself.

$1 \times 12 =$

$2 \times 12 =$

Time taken _____ Seconds

All the answers above are called **multiples** of twelve.

2 Write out the answers to the twelve times table division facts as fast as you can. Time yourself.

$108 \div 12 =$	$132 \div 12 =$	$96 \div 12 =$
$24 \div 12 =$	$48 \div 12 =$	$144 \div 12 =$
$84 \div 12 =$	$12 \div 12 =$	$36 \div 12 =$
$60 \div 12 =$	$72 \div 12 =$	$120 \div 12 =$

Time taken _____ Seconds

There are twelve months in each year.

3 How many months are there altogether in two years?

4 How many years does sixty months make?

5 How many months are there altogether in nine years?

6 How many years does thirty-six months make?

7 How many months are there altogether in twelve years?

8 How many years does seventy-two months make?

9 How many months are there altogether in twenty years?

10 How many years does ninety-six months make?

Complete each set of questions as quickly as you can.

	Set A		Set B		Set C	
1	6 x 6 =		4 x 12 =		6 x 7 =	
2	24 ÷ 6 =		40 ÷ 8 =		64 ÷ 8 =	
3	12 x 7 =		9 x 9 =		12 x 6 =	
4	72 ÷ 8 =		48 ÷ 6 =		42 ÷ 7 =	
5	12 x 9 =		7 x 7 =		30 x 6 =	
6	36 ÷ 6 =		4 x 11 =		20 x 7 =	
7	8 x 7 =		72 ÷ 9 =		40 x 8 =	
8	66 ÷ 6 =		11 x 11 =		80 x 6 =	
9	6 x 9 =		45 ÷ 9 =		30 x 12 =	
10	27 ÷ 9 =		5 x 12 =		90 x 7 =	
11	5 x 8 =		108 ÷ 12 =		70 x 6 =	
12	21 ÷ 7 =		9 x 11 =		40 x 12 =	

13 From a box of ninety-six apples, how many bags of twelve apples can be made?

15 From a box of ninety-six apples, how many bags of six apples can be made?

14 From a box of ninety-six apples, how many bags of eight apples can be made?

16 From a box of ninety-six apples, how many bags of three apples can be made?

It's easy to multiply three-digit numbers by one digit numbers.

Look at this question:

394 x 6

There are three hundreds. | There are nine tens. | There are four units. | We are multiplying by six units.

```
    3  9  4              3  9  4              3  9  4
 x        6           x        6           x        6
 ─────────            ─────────            ─────────
          4                 6  4        2  3  6  4
       2                  5  2              5  2
```

We multiply the 4 units by the 6 units first, which gives us 24, so we write the 4 in the units column and carry the 2 to under the tens column.

Next, we multiply the 9 tens by the 6 units to make 54. Add the 2 tens that were carried over so we now have 56 tens, which are enough for 5 hundreds and 6 tens. We carry the 5 hundreds to underneath the hundreds column.

Finally we multiply the 3 hundreds by the 6 units to give us 18 hundreds. We add the 5 hundreds so that we now have enough for 3 hundreds and 2 thousands.

Now try these.

1 **268 x 7**

3 **726 x 9**

2 **432 x 8**

4 **999 x 9**

Are you getting quicker at short multiplication?

Use short multiplication to answer the questions on this page. The first one has been done for you.

1 543 x 3

		5	4	3
	x			3
	1	6	2	9
			1	

5 347 x 8

2 476 x 6

6 826 x 5

3 678 x 9

7 954 x 4

4 534 x 7

8 763 x 7

Brodie's Fast Five

14 x 9 =

14 x 8 =

14 x 6 =

14 x 4 =

14 x 7 =

These numbers are getting bigger! Read the explanation carefully.

Look at this question:

2374 x 6

There are two thousands.

There are three hundreds.

There are seven tens.

There are four units.

We are multiplying by six units.

We multiply the four units by the six units first, then we work along the top line, multiplying the tens by the six, then the hundreds by the six, and finally the thousands by the six.

1

```
    2  3  7  4
 x           6
 _____
             4
          2
```

2

```
    2  3  7  4
 x           6
 _____
          4  4
       4  2
```

3

```
    2  3  7  4
 x           6
 _____
       2  4  4
    2  4  2
```

4

```
    2  3  7  4
 x           6
 _____
 1  4  2  4  4
    2  4  2
```

Now try these.

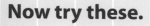

1 3256 x 7

3 4892 x 9

2 6487 x 6

4 7348 x 8

I bet you're getting good at this now!

Use short multiplication to answer the questions on this page. The first question has been done for you.

1 2398 x 4

```
    2   3   9   8
x               4
    9   5   9   2
        1   3   3
```

5 5750 x 8

2 4738 x 6

6 7351 x 5

3 1256 x 9

7 8946 x 4

4 3746 x 7

8 6549 x 7

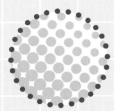

Brodie's Fast Five

10 x 12 =   20 x 12 =

30 x 12 =   40 x 12 =   50 x 12 =

Using short multiplication

Can you solve these problems? You may need to use addition or subtraction as well as multiplication.

There are 365 days in most years. There are 366 days in a leap year. Leap years take place every four years. These years are leap years: 2016, 2020, 2024, 2028, 2032.

1 How many days are there altogether in 2021, 2022 and 2023?

2 How many days are there altogether in 2024, 2025, 2026 and 2027?

3 How many days are there altogether in 2028, 2029, 2030, 2031 and 2032?

There are 2564 sweets in a jar.

4 How many sweets would there be in 4 of these jars if they all hold the same number of sweets?

5 How many sweets would there be in 7 of these jars?

6 How many sweets would there be in 9 of these jars?

Use short multiplication to answer these questions.

1 798 x 3

4 865 x 7

2 699 x 7

5 729 x 9

3 437 x 8

6 216 x 6

7 How many days are there altogether in the years 2021 to 2030?

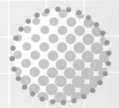

Divisions with remainders

Can you remember what a remainder is?

Sometimes divisions have remainders.
Look at this example:

There are 27 eggs. The eggs need to be sorted into boxes with 6 in each.

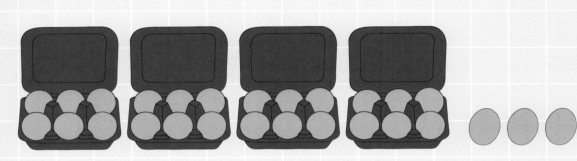

There are enough eggs for 4 boxes of 6 and there are 3 eggs left over.

We can write the mathematical sentence like this: $27 \div 6 = 4 \, r3$

This letter r means remainder.
The remainder shows what is left over.

Now try these.

1 $56 \div 5 =$

2 $28 \div 3 =$

3 $39 \div 4 =$

4 $51 \div 6 =$

5 $47 \div 7 =$

6 $32 \div 5 =$

7 $26 \div 8 =$

8 $64 \div 9 =$

Brodie's Fast Five

$40 \div 2 =$

$50 \div 2 =$

$60 \div 2 =$

$70 \div 2 =$

$80 \div 2 =$

Here is a reminder about short division.

Look at this question:

96 ÷ 3

There are nine tens.   **There are six units.**   **We are dividing by three units.**

To divide 96 by 3, we can write the question out like this:

	3				3	2
3	9	6		3	9	6

First, work out how many times 3 can go into 9. The answer to this is 3. Write write the 3 above the 9.

Next, to divide the 6 units by the 3 units, work out how many times 3 can go into 6. The answer to this is 2. Write the 2 above the 6. The final answer is 32.

Sometimes when we divide the tens there is a spare ten that can be broken into ten extra units.

9 tens divided by 2 is 4 tens, but there is a ten left over that can be used with the 8 units, so that there are 18 units.

Next, divide the 18 units by 2, to give 9 units. The final answer is 49.

Now try these.

1   **84 ÷ 4**

3   **57 ÷ 3**

2   **96 ÷ 4**

4   **76 ÷ 2**

Short division

Now try these! Can you answer them all?

Use short division to answer the questions on this page. The first one has been done for you.

1 87 ÷ 3

$$\begin{array}{r} 2\ \ 9 \\ 3\ \overline{)\ 8\ ^2 7} \end{array}$$

5 90 ÷ 2

2 96 ÷ 4

6 76 ÷ 4

3 85 ÷ 5

7 98 ÷ 7

4 90 ÷ 6

8 72 ÷ 4

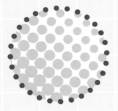

Brodie's Fast Five

77 ÷ 7 =   65 ÷ 5 =

84 ÷ 2 =   132 ÷ 12 =   96 ÷ 2 =

More short division

Look at this question:

$$796 \div 2$$

There are seven hundreds.

There are nine tens.

There are six units.

We are dividing by two units.

To divide 796 by 2, we can write the question out like this:

```
        3                      3  9                    3  9  8
    _____            _____            _____
  2 | 7  ¹9  6           2 | 7  ¹9  ¹6           2 | 7  ¹9  ¹6
```

We divide the 7 hundreds by the 2 units first. 2 goes into 7 three times, with a remainder of 1. We write the 3 in the hundreds column, and carry the remaining 1 over to the tens column to give a total of 19 tens.

Now we divide the 19 tens, giving an answer of 9 for the tens column, and 1 ten carried over to break into units.

Finally we divide the units, to give us 8. The final answer is 398.

Now try these.

1 $824 \div 4$

3 $744 \div 3$

2 $736 \div 4$

4 $864 \div 3$

Brodie's Fast Five

$48 \div 4 =$

$80 \div 4 =$

$60 \div 4 =$

$64 \div 4 =$

$76 \div 4 =$

24

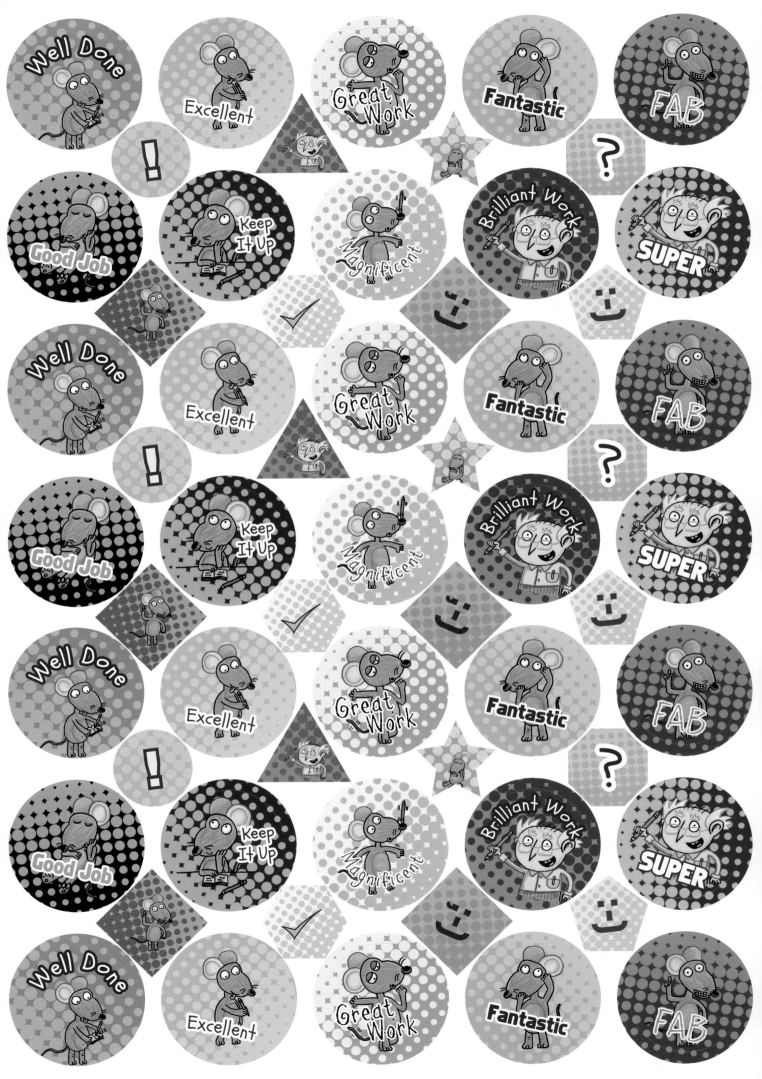

Using short division

Can you solve the problems?

There are 144 children at Sports Day.

1 If the children are put in groups of six, how many groups will there be?

4 If the children are put in groups of three, how many groups will there be?

2 If the children are put in groups of nine, how many groups will there be?

5 If the children are put in groups of four, how many groups will there be?

3 If the children are put in groups of eight, how many groups will there be?

6 If the children are split into two groups, how many children will be in each group?

Brodie's Fast Five

2 x 25 =   3 x 25 =

4 x 25 =   5 x 25 =   6 x 25 =

25

Use short division to answer these questions.

1   68 ÷ 4

5   916 ÷ 2

2   150 ÷ 6

6   792 ÷ 3

3   150 ÷ 2

7   748 ÷ 4

4   728 ÷ 4

8   695 ÷ 5

The questions below have remainders.

9   92 ÷ 5

11   57 ÷ 4

10   29 ÷ 3

12   81 ÷ 6

Short division with remainders

Look carefully at the way we write out a short

Look at this question:

$$87 \div 5$$

There are eight tens.   **There are seven units.**   **We are dividing by five units.**

To divide 87 by 5, we can write the question out like this:

```
        5 | 8  7          →          5 | 8 ³7          →          5 | 8 ³7
```

First step shows `5 | 8 7`. Middle step shows `1` above with `5 | 8 ³7`. Last step shows `1 7 r2` above with `5 | 8 ³7`.

Use short division to answer the questions below.
The first one has been done for you.

1 **73 ÷ 5**

```
        1  4  r3
    5 | 7  ²3
```

4 **312 ÷ 7**

2 **168 ÷ 5**

5 **467 ÷ 8**

3 **195 ÷ 2**

6 **833 ÷ 6**

Brodie's Fast Five

2 x 20 = ___   3 x 20 = ___

4 x 20 = ___   5 x 20 = ___   6 x 20 = ___

27

On this page we are dividing four-digit numbers.

Look at this question:

$$5472 \quad \div \quad 2$$

There are five thousands.

There are four hundreds.

There are seven tens.

There are two units.

We are dividing by two units.

Look at how the question is solved.

1
```
        2
   2 | 5 ¹4  7  2
```

2
```
        2  7
   2 | 5 ¹4  7  2
```

3
```
        2  7  3
   2 | 5 ¹4  7 ¹2
```

4
```
        2  7  3  6
   2 | 5 ¹4  7 ¹2
```

Now try these.

1 2592 ÷ 4

2 3490 ÷ 5

3 2431 ÷ 7

4 5469 ÷ 8

5 6822 ÷ 9

6 8627 ÷ 6

Using short division

Can you solve the problems?

There is going to be a party at school. There are eight places at each table.

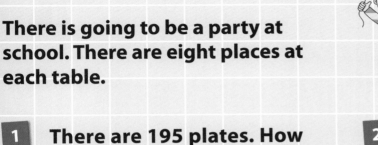

1 There are 195 plates. How many tables can be set up using these plates? Are there any plates left over? Show your workings.

2 There are 650 sandwiches. How many children could have four sandwiches each?

3 There are 418 cupcakes. How many children could have two cupcakes each?

There are 1828 children at the local secondary school.

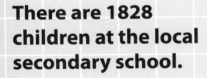

4 How many groups of 8 pupils can be made? How many children will not be in a group of 8? Write your answer as a number with a remainder.

5 How many groups of 6 pupils can be made? How many children will not be in a group of 6? Write your answer as a number with a remainder.

Multiplying by 10

Look at these examples.

$10 \times 6 = 60$ $10 \times 15 = 150$ $10 \times 23 = 230$ $10 \times 47 = 470$

$10 \times 134 = 1340$ $275 \times 10 = 2750$ $469 \times 10 = 4690$

Now look at these.

$7 \times 10 = 70$ $29 \times 10 = 290$ $317 \times 10 = 3170$ $6942 \times 10 = 69420$

Look at this number, shown in columns.

H	T	U		H	T	U
	6	3	If 63 is multiplied by 10 we get	6	3	0

The 3 has moved one place to the left, from the units column to the tens column. The 6 has moved one place to the left, from the tens column to the hundreds column. A zero has been written in the units column.

Now try these.

1 $10 \times 13 =$

2 $10 \times 27 =$

3 $10 \times 192 =$

4 $385 \times 10 =$

5 $10 \times 512 =$

6 $4365 \times 10 =$

We can also multiply decimals by 10.

$10 \times 0.6 = 6$ $10 \times 1.5 = 15$ $10 \times 2.3 = 23$ $10 \times 4.7 = 47$

Did you notice that the units digit has moved one place to the left, into the tens column? Did you notice that the tenths digit moved one place to the left, into the units column?

Brodie's Fast Five

$10 \times 2.6 =$ $3.9 \times 10 =$

$14.6 \times 10 =$ $10 \times 13.8 =$ $45.5 \times 10 =$

Multiplying by 100

Multiplying by 100 is easy too.

Look at these examples.

$$100 \times 6 = 600 \qquad 100 \times 15 = 1500 \qquad 315 \times 100 = 31500$$

$$563 \times 100 = 56300$$

Look at this number, shown in columns.

TTh	Th	H	T	U		TTh	Th	H	T	U
		2	7	6	If 276 is multiplied by 100 we get	2	7	6	0	0

The 6 has moved two places to the left, from the units column to the hundreds column. The 7 has moved two places to the left, from the tens column to the thousands column. The 2 has moved two places to the left, from the hundreds column to the ten thousands column. A zero has been written in the units column and in the tens column.

Now try these.

1   100 x 14 =

2   100 x 38 =

3   154 x 100 =

4   572 x 100 =

5   100 x 750 =

6   2764 x 100 =

We can also multiply decimals by 100.

$$100 \times 0.6 = 60 \qquad 100 \times 1.5 = 150 \qquad 100 \times 2.3 = 230 \qquad 100 \times 4.7 = 470$$

Did you notice that the units digit has moved two places to the left, into the hundreds column? Did you notice that the tenths digit has moved two places to the left, into the tens column?

Brodie's Fast Five

100 x 2.6 =

3.2 x 100 =

17.4 x 100 =

100 x 23.5 =

63.1 x 100 =

Use short division to answer these questions.

| 1 | 6238 ÷ 4 |

| 5 | 9136 ÷ 8 |

| 2 | 2337 ÷ 6 |

| 6 | 9234 ÷ 3 |

| 3 | 4357 ÷ 2 |

| 7 | 4610 ÷ 9 |

| 4 | 8376 ÷ 7 |

| 8 | 6695 ÷ 5 |

Now answer these multiplication questions.

| 9 | 48 x 10 |

| 11 | 39.7 x 10 |

| 10 | 10 x 526 |

| 12 | 100 x 75.2 |

Multiplication by tens explanation page

Look at this question:

$$34 \quad x \quad 20$$

As you know, when we multiply by 10, the digits in the number move one place to the left. We can show this in a formal written multiplication:

Step ❶	Step ❷	Step ❸	Step ❹
Write the numbers above one another.	Write a zero in the units column to automatically move the answer digits to the left.	Multiply the 4 units by the 2 tens and write the 8 in the tens column.	Multiply the 3 tens by the 2 tens and write the 6 in the hundreds column.

	3	4			3	4			3	4			3	4
x	2	0	x		2	0	x		2	0	x		2	0
						0			8	0		6	8	0

Sometimes we need to carry digits to the tens column or the hundreds column.

Look at this question:

$$38 \quad x \quad 70$$

Step ❶	Step ❷	Step ❸	Step ❹
Write the numbers above one another.	Write a zero in the units column to automatically move the answer digits to the left.	Multiply the 8 units by the 7 tens. Write the 6 in the tens column and carry the 5 to the hundreds.	Multiply the 3 tens by the 7 tens. Add the 5, then write the 6 in the hundreds column and carry the 2 straight into the thousands column.

	3	8			3	8			3	8			3	8
x	7	0	x		7	0	x		7	0	x		7	0
						0			6	0	2	6	6	0
								5				5		

Multiplication by tens

 Look carefully at the examples on page 33.

Answer the multiplication questions below.
The first one has been done for you.

1 54 x 30

```
        5   4
    x   3   0
  ─────────────
    1   6   2   0
          1
```

2 47 x 60

3 68 x 90

4 36 x 70

5 239 x 80

6 744 x 40

7 379 x 50

8 763 x 70

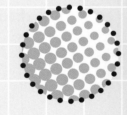

Brodie's Fast Five

10 x 49 =   100 x 8 =

100 x 6.4 =   10 x 7.4 =   14 x 100 =

Long multiplication

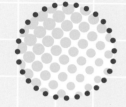

We need to multiply by two digit numbers.

Multiplying two two-digit numbers together is a bit more complex. Look at this question:

$$34 \times 26$$

What we need to do is to multiply 34 by the 6 units first, then multiply by the 2 tens, before adding the two answers together. We can show this in one calculation.

```
        3   4
  x     2   6
  _____
    2   0   4
          2
    6   8   0
  _____
    8   8   4
  _____
```

This row shows the multiplication of 34 x 6.

This row shows the multiplication of 34 x 20. It is important to remember that we are multiplying by 20 and not 2, because the 2 in the question is in the tens column. We therefore need to add a 0 to the units column on this line.

This row shows the two multiplications added together.

Now try these.

1   68 x 43

3   57 x 94

2   43 x 87

4   98 x 62

35

More long multiplication

Remember to add a 0 in the second line of your working!

**Answer the multiplication questions below.
The first one has been done for you.**

1   47 x 36

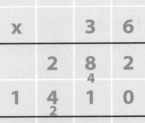

```
        4  7
   x    3  6
      2  8  2
        4
   1  4  1  0
      2
   1  6  9  2
```

2   89 x 27

3   34 x 16

4   55 x 48

5   306 x 26

6   275 x 45

7   488 x 79

8   983 x 38

Using long multiplication

You will need to use multiplication to work out the answer to question 4. Hint: the answer is more than 5 and fewer than 10 coaches.

You may need to use addition or subtraction as well as multiplication.

Cathy's Coach Company has twenty-four 38-seat coaches and seventeen smaller 56-seat coaches.

1 How many seats are there on all of the smaller coaches, in total?

3 What is the total number of seats altogether?

2 How many seats are there on all of the larger coaches, in total?

4 A secondary school has 1247 pupils. All the pupils are travelling to a sports ground. If the school hires all of the 56-seat coaches from Cathy's Coach Company, how many of the 38-seat coaches would also be needed?

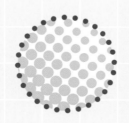

Use short or long multiplication to answer these questions.

1 56 x 7

2 56 x 70

3 56 x 23

4 79 x 40

5 234 x 60

6 68 x 49

7 732 x 56

8 799 x 80

9 275 x 75

10 25 x 25

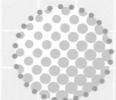

Factors

Can you find the factors of any number?

Look at the ways we can make six by multiplying.

1 x 6   6 x 1

6

3 x 2   2 x 3

1 Write the multiplication facts for each number below.

8

20

9

12

14

16

100

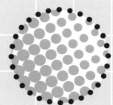

2 The factors of 8 are ___ ___ and ___

3 The factors of 9 are ___ and ___

4 The factors of 12 are ___ ___ and ___

5 The factors of 14 are ___ and ___

6 The factors of 16 are ___ and ___

7 The factors of 20 are ___ and ___

8 The factors of 100 are ___ ___ and ___

39

Prime numbers

Some numbers have only two factors.

Look at the ways we can make seven by multiplying.

1 x 7 — **7** — 7 x 1

The number 1 is a special number. Its only factor is itself.

Prime numbers have two factors. Number 7 is a prime number. It has only two factors: itself and 1. It is not in any multiplication table except its own table, the sevens.

Write the factors for each number below.

1	2		11	12	
2	3				
3	4		12	23	
4	5		13	24	
5	6				
6	7		14	36	
7	8				
8	9				
9	10		15	72	
10	11				

16 Numbers with only two factors, themselves and 1, are called prime numbers. Which of the numbers above are prime numbers?

Here is a way to find prime numbers less than 100.

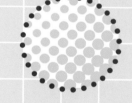

Look at the hundred square.

- Cross out the number 1 because it is not a prime number.
- Leave number 2, as it is a prime number, but cross out every multiple of 2 all the way up to 100.
- Leave number 3, as it is a prime number, but cross out every multiple of 3.
- Leave number 5, as it is a prime number, but cross out every multiple of 5.
- Leave number 7, as it is a prime number, but cross out every multiple of 7.

1	2	3	4	5	6	7	8	9	10
11	12	13	14	15	16	17	18	19	20
21	22	23	24	25	26	27	28	29	30
31	32	33	34	35	36	37	38	39	40
41	42	43	44	45	46	47	48	49	50
51	52	53	54	55	56	57	58	59	60
61	62	63	64	65	66	67	68	69	70
71	72	73	74	75	76	77	78	79	80
81	82	83	84	85	86	87	88	89	90
91	92	93	94	95	96	97	98	99	100

1 Which numbers are not crossed out?

These are the prime numbers.

2 What is the only even prime number?

Square numbers

Multiplying a number by itself makes a square number.

Look at the dot patterns.

One set of one.   Two sets of two.   Three sets of three.   Four sets of four.
$1 \times 1 = 1$ $2 \times 2 = 4$ $3 \times 3 = 9$ $4 \times 4 = 16$

The numbers 1, 4, 9 and 16 are all square numbers.

The next square number is 25.

Look: $5 \times 5 = 25$

We can write this as follows: $5^2 = 25$

Now try these.

1	$6^2 =$	5	$10^2 =$	9	$30^2 =$
2	$7^2 =$	6	$11^2 =$	10	$40^2 =$
3	$8^2 =$	7	$12^2 =$	11	$50^2 =$
4	$9^2 =$	8	$20^2 =$	12	$60^2 =$

You will need to use long multiplication for the next questions.

13   64^2

15   43^2

14   72^2

16   49^2

Cube numbers

Look at the cubes.

This cube is made of **8** small cubes.
It is **2** little cubes wide. It is **2** little cubes deep.
It is **2** little cubes high. **2 x 2 x 2 = 8**

This cube is made of **27** small cubes.
It is **3** little cubes wide. It is **3** little cubes deep.
It is **3** little cubes high. **3 x 3 x 3 = 27**

The numbers 8 and 27 are called cube numbers.
The next cube number is **64**. Look: **4 x 4 x 4 = 64**
We can write this as follows: $4^3 = 64$

Now try these. You may need to use short multiplication or long multiplication to find some of the answers.

1 5^3

2 6^3

3 7^3

4 8^3

5 9^3

6 10^3

7 12^3

8 25^3

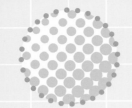

How quickly can you complete all of these questions?

1 What are the factors of 64?

2 Draw a ring around the prime number:

   12   13   14   15   16

3 What are the factors of 100?

4 Draw a ring around the prime number:

   32   36   37   39

5 What are the factors of 144?

6 Draw a ring around the prime number:

   72   73   74   75   76

Use short multiplication to answer the questions.

7 25^2

9 8^3

8 36^2

10 25^3

ANSWERS

Page 3 • Practising the two times table

1.
   1 x 2 = 2
   2 x 2 = 4
   3 x 2 = 6
   4 x 2 = 8
   5 x 2 = 10
   6 x 2 = 12
   7 x 2 = 14
   8 x 2 = 16
   9 x 2 = 18
   10 x 2 = 20
   11 x 2 = 22
   12 x 2 = 24

2.
   1
   2
   3
   4
   5
   6
   7
   8
   9
   10
   11
   12

3. 16
4. 12
5. 22
6. 9
7. 30
8. 20

Page 4 • Practising the three times table

1.
   1 x 3 = 3
   2 x 3 = 6
   3 x 3 = 9
   4 x 3 = 12
   5 x 3 = 15
   6 x 3 = 18
   7 x 3 = 21
   8 x 3 = 24
   9 x 3 = 27
   10 x 3 = 30
   11 x 3 = 33
   12 x 3 = 36

2.
   1
   12
   4
   9
   2
   11
   7
   3
   6
   10
   5
   8

3. 21
4. 8
5. 36
6. 6
7. 27
8. 12
9. 90
10. 20

Page 5 • Practising the four times table

1.
   1 x 4 = 4
   2 x 4 = 8
   3 x 4 = 12
   4 x 4 = 16
   5 x 4 = 20
   6 x 4 = 24
   7 x 4 = 28
   8 x 4 = 32
   9 x 4 = 36
   10 x 4 = 40
   11 x 4 = 44
   12 x 4 = 48

2.
   12
   9
   4
   1
   6
   10
   3
   2
   11
   8
   5
   7

3. 32
4. 6
5. 48
6. 4
7. 36
8. 9
9. 80
10. 15

Page 6 • Practising the five times table

1.
   1 x 5 = 5
   2 x 5 = 10
   3 x 5 = 15
   4 x 5 = 20
   5 x 5 = 25
   6 x 5 = 30
   7 x 5 = 35
   8 x 5 = 40
   9 x 5 = 45
   10 x 5 = 50
   11 x 5 = 55
   12 x 5 = 60

2.
   10
   12
   3
   5
   1
   6
   11
   8
   7
   4
   9
   2

3. 45
4. 5
5. 30
6. 11
7. 60
8. 13
9. 75
10. 20

Page 7 • Practising the six times table

1.
   1 x 6 = 6
   2 x 6 = 12
   3 x 6 = 18
   4 x 6 = 24
   5 x 6 = 30
   6 x 6 = 36
   7 x 6 = 42
   8 x 6 = 48
   9 x 6 = 54
   10 x 6 = 60
   11 x 6 = 66
   12 x 6 = 72

2.
   6
   11
   3
   4
   7
   9
   12
   10
   2
   5
   1
   8

3. 54
4. 4
5. 36
6. 11
7. 72
8. 7
9. 90
10. 14

Page 8 • Progress Test 1

	Set A	Set B	Set C
1.	12	16	36
2.	12	10	10
3.	24	36	72
4.	9	12	7
5.	36	28	60
6.	11	16	69
7.	24	3	36
8.	2	55	320
9.	18	9	150
10.	9	25	180
11.	15	12	420
12.	7	45	160

13. 10
14. 5
15. 6
16. 15

Page 9 • Practising the seven times table

1.
   1 x 7 = 7
   2 x 7 = 14
   3 x 7 = 21
   4 x 7 = 28
   5 x 7 = 35
   6 x 7 = 42
   7 x 7 = 49
   8 x 7 = 56
   9 x 7 = 63
   10 x 7 = 70
   11 x 7 = 77
   12 x 7 = 84

2. 7
   10
   2
   1
   8
   9
   3
   6
   5
   12
   11
   4

3. 28
4. 8
5. 63
6. 10
7. 42
8. 5
9. 140
10. 20

Page 10 • Practising the eight times table

1. 1 x 8 = 8
   2 x 8 = 16
   3 x 8 = 24
   4 x 8 = 32
   5 x 8 = 40
   6 x 8 = 48
   7 x 8 = 56
   8 x 8 = 64
   9 x 8 = 72
   10 x 8 = 80
   11 x 8 = 88
   12 x 8 = 96

2. 8
   11
   3
   9
   5
   2
   1
   7
   12
   6
   10
   4

3. 32
4. 7
5. 72
6. 12
7. 64
8. 20
9. 112
10. 25

Page 11 • Practising the nine times table

1. 1 x 9 = 9
   2 x 9 = 18
   3 x 9 = 27
   4 x 9 = 36
   5 x 9 = 45
   6 x 9 = 54
   7 x 9 = 63
   8 x 9 = 72
   9 x 9 = 81
   10 x 9 = 90
   11 x 9 = 99
   12 x 9 = 108

2. 6
   5
   11
   3
   7
   12
   1
   8
   2
   10
   4
   9

3. 27
4. 6
5. 99
6. 9
7. 72
8. 13
9. 126
10. 20

Page 12 • Practising the eleven times table

1. 1 x 11 = 11
   2 x 11 = 22
   3 x 11 = 33
   4 x 11 = 44
   5 x 11 = 55
   6 x 11 = 66
   7 x 11 = 77
   8 x 11 = 88
   9 x 11 = 99
   10 x 11 = 110
   11 x 11 = 121
   12 x 11 = 132

2. 11
   2
   6
   3
   1
   5
   10
   8
   7
   4
   9
   12

3. 88
4. 2
5. 33
6. 9
7. 121
8. 10
9. 132
10. 7

Page 13 • Practising the twelve times table

1. 1 x 12 = 12
   2 x 12 = 24
   3 x 12 = 36
   4 x 12 = 48
   5 x 12 = 60
   6 x 12 = 72
   7 x 12 = 84
   8 x 12 = 96
   9 x 12 = 108
   10 x 12 = 120
   11 x 12 = 132
   12 x 12 = 144

2. 9
   2
   7
   5
   11
   4
   1
   6
   8
   12
   3
   10

3. 24
4. 5
5. 108
6. 3
7. 144
8. 6
9. 240
10. 8

Page 14 • Progress Test 2

	Set A	Set B	Set C
1.	36	48	42
2.	4	5	8
3.	84	81	72
4.	9	8	6
5.	108	49	180
6.	6	44	140
7.	56	8	320
8.	11	121	480
9.	54	5	360
10.	3	60	630
11.	40	9	420
12.	3	99	480

13. 8
14. 12
15. 16
16. 32

Page 15 • Short multiplication of three-digit numbers

1. 1876
2. 3456
3. 6534
4. 8991

Page 16 • More short multiplication of three-digit numbers

1. 1629
2. 2856
3. 6102
4. 3738
5. 2776
6. 4130
7. 3816
8. 5341

Brodie's Fast Five

1. 126
2. 112
3. 84
4. 56
5. 98

Page 17 • Short multiplication of four-digit numbers

1. 22792
2. 38922
3. 44028
4. 58784

Page 18 • More short multiplication of four-digit numbers

1. 9592
2. 28428
3. 11304
4. 26222
5. 46000
6. 36755
7. 35784
8. 45843

Brodie's Fast Five

1. 120
2. 240
3. 360
4. 480
5. 600

Page 19 • Using short multiplication

1. 1095
2. 1461
3. 1827
4. 10256
5. 17948
6. 23076

Brodie's Fast Five

1. 700
2. 500
3. 900
4. 800
5. 1200

Page 20 • Progress Test 3

1. 2394
2. 4893
3. 3496
4. 6055
5. 6561
6. 1296
7. 3652

Page 21 • Divisions with remainders

1. 11 r1
2. 9 r1
3. 9 r3
4. 8 r3
5. 6 r5
6. 6 r2
7. 3 r2
8. 7 r1

Brodie's Fast Five

1. 20
2. 25
3. 30
4. 35
5. 40

Page 22 • Short division explanation page

1. 21
2. 24
3. 19
4. 76

Page 23 • Short division

1. 29
2. 24
3. 17
4. 15
5. 45
6. 19
7. 14
8. 18

Brodie's Fast Five

1. 11
2. 13
3. 42
4. 11
5. 48

Page 24 • More short division

1. 206
2. 184
3. 248
4. 288

Brodie's Fast Five

1. 12
2. 20
3. 15
4. 16
5. 19

Page 25 • Using short division

1. 24
2. 16
3. 18
4. 48
5. 36
6. 72

Brodie's Fast Five

1. 50
2. 75
3. 100
4. 125
5. 150

Page 26 • Progress Test 4

1. 17
2. 25
3. 75
4. 182
5. 458
6. 264
7. 187
8. 139
9. 18 r2
10. 9 r2
11. 14 r1
12. 13 r3

Page 27 • Short division with remainders

1. 14 r3
2. 33 r3
3. 97 r1
4. 44 r4
5. 58 r3
6. 138 r5

Brodie's Fast Five

1. 40
2. 60
3. 80
4. 100
5. 120

Page 28 • Short division of four-digit numbers

1. 648
2. 698
3. 347 r2
4. 683 r5
5. 758
6. 1437 r5

Page 29 • Using short division

1. 24 tables can be set up with 8 places. There will be 3 plates left over.
2. 162 children could have 4 sandwiches each. There will be 2 spare sandwiches.
3. 209 children could have 2 cupcakes each.
4. There will be 228 groups of 8. Four children will not be in a group.
5. There will be 304 groups of 6. Four children will not be in a group.

Page 30 • Multiplying by 10

1. 130
2. 270
3. 1920
4. 3850
5. 5120
6. 43650

Brodie's Fast Five

1. 26
2. 39
3. 146
4. 138
5. 455

Page 31 • Multiplying by 100

1. 1400
2. 3800
3. 15400
4. 57200
5. 75000
6. 276400

Brodie's Fast Five

1. 260
2. 320
3. 1740
4. 2350
5. 6310

Page 32 • Progress Test 5

1. 1559 r2
2. 389 r3
3. 2178 r1
4. 1196 r4
5. 1142
6. 3078
7. 512 r2
8. 1339
9. 480
10. 5260
11. 397
12. 7520

Page 34 • Multiplication by tens

1. 1620
2. 2820
3. 6120
4. 2520
5. 19120
6. 29760
7. 18950
8. 53410

Brodie's Fast Five

1. 490
2. 800
3. 640
4. 74
5. 1400

Page 35 • Long multiplication

1. 2924
2. 3741
3. 5358
4. 6076

Brodie's Fast Five

1. 100
2. 1000
3. 10000
4. 10000
5. 100000

Page 36 • More long multiplication

1. 1692
2. 2403
3. 544
4. 2640
5. 7956
6. 12375
7. 38552
8. 37354

Page 37 • Using long multiplication

1. 912
2. 952
3. 1864
4. 8

Page 38 • Progress Test 6

1. 392
2. 3920
3. 1288
4. 3160
5. 14040
6. 3332
7. 40992
8. 63920
9. 20625
10. 625

Page 39 • Factors

1. eight: 1 x 8, 8 x 1, 2 x 4, 4 x 2
   twenty: 1 x 20, 20 x 1, 2 x 10,
   10 x 2, 4 x 5, 5 x 4
   nine: 1 x 9, 9 x 1 , 3 x 3
   twelve: 1 x 12, 12 x 1, 6 x 2,
   2 x 6, 3 x 4, 4 x 3
   fourteen: 1 x 14, 14 x 1, 2 x 7,
   7 x 2
   sixteen: 1 x 16, 16 x 1, 2 x 8,
   8 x 2, 4 x 4
   100: 1 x 100, 100 x 1, 10 x 10,
   20 x 5, 5 x 20, 25 x 4, 4 x 25,
   2 x 50, 50 x 2

2. 1 2 4 8
3. 1 3 9
4. 1 2 3 4 6 12
5. 1 2 7 14
6. 1 2 4 8 16
7. 1 2 4 5 10 20
8. 1 2 4 5 10 20 25 50 100

Page 40 • Prime numbers

1. 1 2
2. 1 3
3. 1 2 4
4. 1 5
5. 1 2 3 6
6. 1 7
7. 1 2 4 8
8. 1 3 9
9. 1 2 5 10
10. 1 11
11. 1 2 3 4 6 12
12. 1 23
13. 1 2 3 4 6 8 12 24
14. 1 2 3 4 6 9 12 18 36
15. 1 2 3 4 6 8 9 12 18 24 36
    72
16. 2 3 5 7 11 23

Page 41 • Finding all the prime numbers up to 100

1. 2 3 5 7 11 13 17 19 23 29
   31 37 41 43 47 53 59 61 67
   71 73 79 83 89 97
2. 2

Page 42 • Square numbers

1. 36
2. 49
3. 64
4. 81
5. 100
6. 121
7. 144
8. 400
9. 900
10. 1600
11. 2500
12. 3600
13. 4096
14. 5184
15. 1849
16. 2401

Page 43 • Cube numbers

1. 125
2. 216
3. 343
4. 512
5. 729
6. 1000
7. 1728
8. 15625

Page 44 • Progress Test 7

1. 1 2 4 8 16 32 64
2. 12 (13) 14 15 16
3. 1 2 4 5 10 20 25 50 100
4. 32 36 (37) 39
5. 1 2 3 4 6 8 9 12 16 18 24
   36 48 72 144
6. 72 (73) 74 75 76
7. 625
8. 1296
9. 512
10. 15625